A DOVE IN SANTIAGO

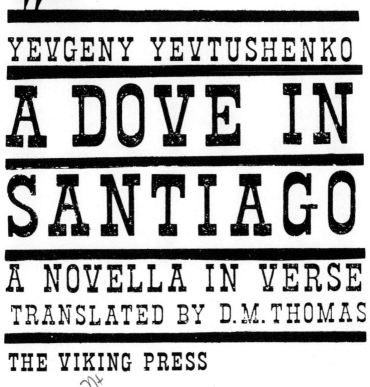

YEVGENY YEVTUSHENKO

A DOVE IN SANTIAGO

A NOVELLA IN VERSE
TRANSLATED BY D.M. THOMAS

THE VIKING PRESS

Originally published in the Soviet literary journal *Novy Mir* in 1978.

Copyright © Yevgeni Yevtushenko 1982

Translation copyright © D. M. Thomas 1982
All rights reserved
Published in 1983 by The Viking Press
625 Madison Avenue, New York, N.Y. 10022

Library of Congress Catalog Card Number: 82-60236
ISBN: 0-670-28070-4

Printed in Great Britain

Translator's Note

A Dove in Santiago was first published in 1978, in the Soviet literary journal *Novy Mir*. The original is in blank verse. I have kept a flexible form of the same metre as the basis of this English version, moving into free verse from time to time, when it seemed appropriate. This approach, I came to believe, offered the best hope of being faithful — or as little unfaithful as possible — to the spirit of the original work.

I wish to thank Jan Yevtushenko, the poet's wife, for providing a literal translation, as an aid to my imperfect knowledge of Russian. Her translation made my task much lighter than it otherwise would have been; and also often, by a particularly expressive turn of phrase, pointed the way to a solution to one problem or another.

D.M.T.

Can I ask my book if I wrote it?

Pablo Neruda

1

Fatigue of the weariest body weighs so little
Compared with the soul's, but if the two join forces
You haven't the strength even to cry . . . And when
You are too tired to cry, then is the time
You especially want to . . . That's how tired I was
One time . . .
                    Of what?
                              Of life? No, not of life,
It's above accusations. I was tired of all
I had found in it that resembled death, not life.
A man doesn't die all at once, but gradually,
Of other people's diseases — indifference,
Cruelty. And pitiable is the man
Who slowly dies, infected by such ills —
For he not only dies himself but, dead,
Can spread the infection to others. Many small deaths
Hide in a telephone-receiver where
It's shameful to phone, and yet there's no way out —
You've got to. In my wretched telephone-book
There are many numbers like that; it's loathsome, sticking
Your finger in the dial, as if the number
You're calling is death's, as if you're opening
A heavy safe you know to be empty except
For a few skulls and bones. That day, I remember,
I had to make several phone-calls that were pointless
Yet necessary. That word stinks of a privy
Where you tread in something foul. Later you can't
Scrape it off your shoes, that shit you've trodden in.
And I phoned, stumbling on voices, sadistically sweet
As honey sometimes, a thick buzzing of flies
Had fallen into it, feet upwards; and sometimes babbling,
Like dough afraid of the pan and giving out
Cowardly bubbles. Oh, the vile, elegant art
Of avoiding a decision and thereby
Deciding people's fates by not deciding.
And every time, I hopelessly put down
The telephone — the dumb-bell of the weak.

I still had to make one call. The telephone
Revolted me suddenly, like a plastic toad.
I couldn't make the call . . .

       I dragged myself
To the sofa, and fell on it face down, too tired
To take my shoes off, forced my hand to pick up
A book from the chair and open it, but the words
Swam. And it wasn't just any book, it was Pushkin.
Are even immortals incapable of helping
Us mortals? Is the voice down the receiver
Really stronger than Homer, Dante, and Shakespeare,
And Pushkin?

     Oh, if even Pushkin can't help,
That's a bad sign. And the thought of suicide crept
Into me from the holes of the receiver,
Like the snake from the horse's skull, the death of Oleg.
I hate this thought in me. It came, like a flirt,
To me in my youth, pleasantly gratifying
My vanity: "Suicide won't kill you —
It will only make you famous. Get yourself known
By killing yourself. Then they'll appreciate you."
(They, they . . . a helpful word for the feeble-hearted,
And, incidentally, for those who come,
Themselves, under the comforting heading of "they".)
Now this coquettish thought had become a hag,
Appearing to me at times, with yellow-stained teeth,
Hiding the snake's subtle venom, and taunting me:
"Don't try, my sweetheart, you can't get away . . . "
I've even grown accustomed to the hag,
And got the better of her, by despising her,
And possibly by knowing her so well.

I don't suppose there's anyone on earth
Who hasn't considered taking his own life.
Mind you, I did know a song-writer who was stuffed
With joviality like straw, and I recall
Him chuckling about a certain tragic affair
That ended with a bankrupt's bullet: "The fool!

I'd never do that. It's never entered my head."
But then, in general, nothing had entered his head.
I lay in the broad daylight as in darkness,
Not seeing the letters of the open book,
But feeling with every wrinkle of my brow
The cold gaze of the old hag's colourless eyes
Fixed on me; she bided her time in silence.
And suddenly, I felt something warm on my forehead,
As if an invisible sunbeam was striking me
From a mischievous boy's mirror. The darkness vanished,
And with it the hag. What brought about the change?
The apartment was empty.
                              Only a dove
Outside, scraping at my window with its beak;
Like a patch of the sky, or maybe a shade darker.
It was perched on the window-ledge; its eyes were almost
Human, and not a feather of it resembled
The well-fed parasites in the square below;
But like a little ruffled friend
Who had flown to save me from death.
And perhaps it had flown from Chile?

2

The word "Chile" evokes pain.
Alas, the more beautiful a country,
The greater the pain when enemies of beauty
Take possession of it. Envious and malicious,
Incurable moral cripples lust to own
At least the body of beauty.
Seducers don't care about the soul.

Let's return to Chile, in '72.
I was staying at the Hotel Carrera
Opposite the presidential palace.
"Allende" and "palace" contradict each other.
Allende contradicted many things,
And what was perhaps most dangerous —
He went against the narrow-minded concept
Of what a president should be.
That contradiction killed him.
Allende was a fine man,
Perhaps too fine. There are those who can't forgive this,
For whom anything good is dangerous.
They fear an intelligent man, and forgive the fool.
Allende was more intelligent than his killers,
But he lacked the intelligence of the tyrant,
Who knows one must stop at nothing.
Allende was destroyed by his own virtue,
Which makes him a survivor, an immortal;
Dead, he is stronger than when he was alive.
When some extremists came to see him
With a list of ten thousand
Who had to be got rid of instantly
(Pinochet was among them), he explained:
"It's easy to shoot people,
But what if even one is innocent?
I don't think you or I
Have the gift of resurrection.
You can't make mistakes with another's life
When you can't resurrect him if mistaken . . . "

"That's suicide!" shouted an extremist,
Reeking of tobacco and dynamite. —
"If we don't kill them, they'll kill us.
Permit us one per cent of a mistake;
You don't make revolutions in kid-gloves."
"As you can see, I don't wear gloves,
But I keep my hands clean.
Lightly to kill someone — that's suicide.
All the tyrants in the world have killed themselves.
I won't commit a suicide of this kind.
Ninety-nine per cent of human justice
Is tainted by that one per cent of crime.
Innocent blood on the right road
Changes the course of that road,
And then it can't be right . . . "
Their comrade, the president, spoke to them calmly,
In his cheap check shirt, with his face
Of a country-doctor, sure of his remedies,
So unlike his official portrait, dress-suit with sash;
Only the sash was really right,
That deep red presidential sash,
That honest sash no drop of blood had stained
Disreputably. But the extremists
Wouldn't listen to Allende, nor had they read
Dostoievsky's *Devils*. Their home-grown terror
Began to seem like the face of socialism,
A face that terrified the bourgeoisie.
Everything split apart. People would go
Quietly into cinemas, courteously,
But as soon as Allende appeared
In documentary images on the screen,
Half the audience in the shadowy darkness
Whistled, howled, stamped their feet, booed,
The other half clapped so loudly
I knew their cause was doomed.
The lights went on. Instantly the storm
That had blown up in the dark subsided.
Everything is less clear in the blazing light;

Everything in life is clearer where it's darker.
I saw a meeting near the palace
Where there was also rather too much light
To make out clearly who was on whose side.
Hands waving torches, and projectors,
Created the light in darkness; but even the hands
In a vast square aren't everyone's hands.
There are hands in reserve, to betray and murder.
Such hands, if the hour has not yet struck,
Will caress cats and children
And even heartily applaud
Those they intend to kill — in gratitude,
As it were, for not being killed.
Allende was no orator, he lacked
The showman's sleight-of-hand the crowd adores,
Wishing to be deceived. Allende had no wish
To deceive either the square or the country.
He tried to deceive himself by affirming too often,
In that speech which was inevitably his last,
His dying words, how loyal his generals were,
By repetition trying to make them so.
They stood behind him, their hairy hands tensed
To applaud him and betray him.
The square lifted its torches towards the sky,
Torches made out of rolled-up newspapers;
And suddenly I saw in one hand,
Raised high in honour of the president,
His slowly disintegrating photograph
Edged with golden-black ash,
As if in a shrinking memorial frame.
The frame grew smaller, and the face vanished.
I shivered and grew uneasy,
Although Allende was standing on the rostrum
Alive, but with the alarming reflection of flares
Flickering in his glasses. Afterwards
The square emptied swiftly; only the dead rostrum,
Knocked up in a hurry, creaked in the darkness,
Only the street doves wandered

Among the ash left by the crowd's flares,
Cautiously pecking at it, as if
They might find something in it . . .

It was one of those doves, perhaps,
Which flew to my rescue in Moscow?
There are too many small histories
Lost within the history of the world
For historians to be able to cope with them.
We need more historians. It's suicidal
To know everything,
But ignorance is suicidal too,
And worse — cowardly. Life without knowledge
Is a dead rostrum. Life is made up of lives,
And history is the link between them all.

3

The morning after the meeting in the square,
I was telephoned in my room.

A woman's voice,
With a Spanish accent on *ch,* was asking if
She might speak with Comrade Señor Yevtuchenko;
"Forgive me, am I too early? May I come up?
I've a manuscript I'd like to show you." I thought
With horror — a poetess. I never know what
To say to them. Whether Russian or Chilean,
They scare me, these strange creatures who put words
Into neat metrical patterns and twist rhymes
The way they put their hair into curlers at night.
There are too few women poets in the world,
But all too many of these poetesses.
I fill with animal fear
As I wait to be sprayed by emotion like a shower.
But the woman who entered my room
Didn't look like a poetess. I had avoided
That particular peril. But then another unease
Took possession of me — what if I was faced
More fearfully still

with a woman novelist?
My visitor saw that I was apprehensive
And, guessing the reason for it, she hurriedly said:
"I don't write myself . . . I've brought you a diary
To read — all that is left of my only son,
Who took his life, and he was only twenty . . ."
She was, I guessed, in her early forties, still
Almost beautiful, with a dark Creole beauty,
In a black mantilla, a severe black dress,
And a Catholic cross was glittering on her neck
Where there were no betraying wrinkles,
And the grey streak in her black hair
Sparkled like the curl of a waterfall.
The woman came closer to me, sighed, warily
Extended a hand in a black transparent glove
As if she was afraid to give to me

The exercise-book, which was also in mournful black.
I said to her: "You can leave it with me . . . I'll read it."
The woman was firm: "Please read it while I'm here.
I'm not in a hurry. I'll wait. My son loved you.
He heard you reading with Neruda.
When you open it, you will understand everything,
And perhaps you'll write a poem
Saying how wrong it is to take one's life,
How self-deceiving. It's something that must be said."

And I opened the diary and commenced reading
The anguished story of a stranger's soul,
Yet is there such a thing as a stranger's soul
When, so often, there isn't a soul around? . . .
The purest of souls laid itself bare to me.
The dead boy was, as they say, thin-skinned,
Transparent and defenceless; I could see
Through his diary the pulsing of every fibre,
The slightest quiver of his heart,
Like a dove, born for the sky,
But trapped in a cramped rib-cage; my finger-tips
Felt they were touching jagged nerves, not lines,
As the letters vibrated under my hand.

4

Enrique was only eight years old
When his father, a linguist and a womaniser
(Which sounds milder in Spanish — *mujeriego*),
Left his mother and married a woman
Whose husband was a diplomat
And not a linguist, but also a *mujeriego*;
And in desperation his mother hurriedly married
An antique-furniture dealer, who,
As fate would have it, was also a *mujeriego*.
His father at first seemed happy,
But gradually his new wife, like a new toy,
Began to bore him; with cruel curiosity
He cracked open his not-so-new toy
And found, inside, her simple mechanism,
And the springs of stupidity and affectation
Which were so rosily disguised
By the smooth, celluloid, well-cared-for skin.
It was then he began to miss his son.
Enrique's mother realised her new version,
In the person of the antique dealer, was old,
Made worse by the fact that he went after women,
And was, moreover, jealous. Most of all
He was jealous of his step-son. Taking her son,
She'd climb into her Volkswagen, and visit the ocean,
Whose face was changeable but never betrayed,
Like the face of Neruda's poems
Which she read aloud to her son. The heavy green breakers
Hurled at their feet, as they walked across the sand,
Mane-like seaweed, jellyfish parachutes,
Dark bottle fragments, so gently rounded by
The sea you could mistake them for emeralds,
And pebbles whose value
Was hidden in their shapes, not in their names.
Enrique's mother started to collect pebbles —
Simply, at first, to put them in a saucer,
With the water which transformed them, to create
A little of the ocean in her home.

Then she took lessons in stone-polishing
From a craftsman and a drunkard, and the pebbles
Talked to her, then, as no one else had done.
More than pebbles, Enrique loved the ocean,
The sea you couldn't capture in a saucer,
Strong in that it didn't know its strength,
And never knew what it might do next.
It's a drag — always behaving well.
It's a bore to behave badly on purpose.
But it's wonderful not to know what you'll do next.
Quite simply, you should live as the ocean does.
As a child, Enrique began to draw, and he liked
The way his brush did not know how to behave
And didn't know what to do next, either.
But his mother was the first to interfere,
Saying of her portrait in water-colour:
"I'm not so old as that, you know . . .
I didn't know you could be so cruel.
Art should make life more beautiful, but you . . .
But you . . ." And his mother ran off crying
To seek refuge at her alcoholic craftsman's,
To polish beach pebbles. And the boy's step-father,
Crammed with ideas about furniture, including
Beds and their warm contents, muttered, "Crap! . . .
You'd do better to draw money, kid."
Everyone's a connoisseur of art;
The ignorant don't dabble in chemistry,
Microbiology or quarks. Restraining
Her tears, the mother of an astronaut
Can only say, "Take care in space, son . . ."
But everyone knows the way it shouldn't be done,
How not to do it, in literature and art,
Though harder for them to say what should be done.

And strangely enough, the first to like Enrique's *crap*
Was the man who had first inflicted a wound
In the little boy's heart — his father. Only when
He'd abandoned his son did he really begin to love him.

He aged. He immersed himself in Sanskrit,
Divorced his wife, and lost his mistresses
Gradually, as they noticed his bald pate,
Expanding paunch, or general lack of prospects.
And he clung to his son as a sign of hope
That he could love someone and be loved;
But people who are egoists in love
Are egoists as fathers, too. Remembering
Him only with his pocket for ten years,
One day he saw a student, a young man
With his family's almond eyes,
Who had grown up without him;
And rather belatedly he began to want
To instil in him all that had grown musty,
Mouldy, rotten, in him — the father . . .
But *had* been in him, truly; so long ago
That hardly anyone remembered it.
He wanted to remind his son
How talented he once had been, himself,
And to convince him that his talent
Came from his father's genes, and not his mother's.
Enrique's mother, not altogether fairly,
Was outraged by this flare-up
Of fatherly affection, calling it
Hypocrisy, not altogether fairly.
She gave the womanless *mujeriego*
A piece of her mind, forbidding him
To see her son. And he responded that his son
Should come to live with him,
His step-father being so insensitive,
As wooden as the furniture he sold.
When two adults batter each other's heads
With their child, the child's head gets broken.
The mother was frightened. They made peace.
It was agreed the object of their fight,
While continuing to live at home,
Would spend each Saturday with his father.
Enrique knew he'd been

Abandoned by his father, but because
He sensed his father's desolation
He loved his father with a father's love;
And every time he left for home, his father
Watched him go out of sight, with a dog's gaze;
And sometimes Enrique stayed, killing his mother,
And went away early on the Monday morning,
And killed his father by leaving, so
Becoming a murderer against his will.

5

Enrique was eighteen when a forty-year-old
Actress friend of his mother looked at him
Suddenly in a special way, as if
She had not noticed him before, and said:
"How tall you've grown!" On stage, or at receptions,
She managed to disguise her fading beauty,
But knew that what she could conceal today
Would be less easy to conceal tomorrow.
In the beauty parlour, wearing a strawberry mask,
She would lie on a hard couch, and the mulatto
Masseuse's muscles were as disciplined
As boxers' when her two slippery black fists
Pounded on the vulnerable back:
"Calm yourself, Señora, it's only rain . . ."
Then her fingers penetrated into
The neck-folds, seeking out the nerve-ends . . .
"Señora, you must relax; it's only lightning!"
But the youth's awkward gaze seemed suddenly
A lightning-flash when — in an unchildlike way
For the first time in his life — his eyes met hers.
As we inevitably age, the adulation
Of a young man or woman works on our vanities
Like a massage. At first like gentle rain,
But as the body weakens and gives way,
The lightning pierces it. We're blinded by
That light and — for however short a time —
Are happy to be blinded, not to see
The horror of our ageing. There's a price
We have to pay — others may fall out
Of love with us, just when we can't stop loving.

One day she rang him, saying she was ill
In bed, and asking him to bring a book.
If possible, a nineteenth century Russian
Novel. He brought *The Brothers Karamazov*
To her, amidst shouts of "Allende for President!"
He rang the bell. He heard a soft call: "It's

Not locked." He entered, in confusion, holding
Before him, with both hands, the novel which
Seemed suddenly very heavy. But of course
He didn't know its real weight as yet.
He saw her lying on a sofa, covered
By a thin sheet that traced her body's outline,
And her head was wrapped in a wet towel.
A strange, dull light shone in her eyes; her hands
Twitched feverishly at the sheet, under her chin.
"Sit down . . ." Her eyes directed him to a chair.
"So that's the book you've brought me. Have you read it?"
"I've started it . . ." "You're only at the start
Of everything in your life . . . How lucky you are
Not to have read that book for the first time.
My eyes are aching. Will you read to me?
— From anywhere at all: about Alyosha . . ."
"I couldn't read it with expression."

                          She laughed,
Like one of the witches in *Macbeth*, her face
Hidden beneath the sheet. Nothing betrays
Wrinkles so much as laughter. "Who taught you that?
What does it mean — with expression? Expression
Is in the words themselves, when they have meaning.
You've picked it up from some teacher, I suppose,
Or some idiotic ham-actor.
How can you improve a work of genius
By reading it with expression, for God's sake?
It's quite enough if you don't spoil the meaning."
Enrique grew even more confused. She made
Him draw his chair up closer, and began
To read to him, as if the book was not
In her hands, as if the words were being spoken
For the first time. He found himself wishing to kiss —
Not her lips, but the words; and leaned towards her
So maladroitly his mouth caught her chin
And he leapt back in fright. She let the book
Fall slowly, took his face between her hands,
Drew it gently towards hers, towards her eyes

Which seemed so huge, and opened his lips with hers,
And the boy's breath was lost in her moist breath.
For ages, sitting beside her, he breathed her warm
And scented breath, and burned with shame because
He wanted her so much. "Lie down with me . . ."
She said. He wondered, horrified, how he
Was going to unlace his shoes, and unzip his trousers,
Without becoming an object of ridicule.
She, as if sensing by instinct how he felt,
Gently and matter-of-factly helped him.
Shivering with cold, his teeth chattering,
He felt embarrassed at his nakedness
Before the enigma of a naked woman.
Quivering with love and fear, he realised
He wasn't able to do anything.
He had wanted to, too much. He sobbed, disgusted
With himself, and huddled his head against
Her small, empty breasts. A single wounding word
From her, and everything might have been changed
For him, it might have sown a hatred of women.
But a woman in love can't help but feel maternal
Towards her man. "Why are you crying, darling?
Everything will be all right . . . Don't worry . . ."
She whispered, and so made it possible
For him to love the women he'd not yet met,
In whom she would be loved again by him
When he had completely ceased to love her.
Without the irksome clumsiness of the body,
She nestled so lovingly against him that
Her gentleness made him strong
And he experienced for the first time the wonder
Of a man and a woman becoming one.

There is a lesson in our first act of love
That's more important than a lesson for the body —
Because the body teaches the soul in it.
When I observe the repulsive chill in the eyes
Of a cynic, I suspect he learnt his cynicism

From the first woman with whom he slept.
But then, who made that woman cynical
If it wasn't the cynic who first slept with her?
It's a marvel the whole earth is not cynical . . .
All the good and noble qualities of men
Come from our mothers, and from our first women,
In whom there is also something from their mothers.

Enrique was grateful to his first woman.
His gratitude made her afraid, and he was afraid
That he was simply grateful to her. A woman's
Last love is sorrow pretending to be hope,
And there is nothing more hopeless in the world
Than sorrow trying to be hopeful.
She loved him fatally, and understood
Its fatality, trying to comfort herself
By murmuring, "What's meant to be, will be . . .
Another five years . . . And then . . . and then . . .
    and then . . ."

The laws of time, stronger than divination,
Elected Allende president.
Victor Hara, with his blazing eyes,
Sang at Che Guevara's monument.
Allende didn't know he was going to be killed.
The immortal hero's statue didn't guess
That it would be destroyed and melted down.
The hands on the guitar did not foretell
That they would be cut off. Enrique
Didn't know what would happen to him. But someone knew,
Hiding his face, because of the heavy knowledge,
In the clouds hanging above the swaying mass
Of people, and his expression was sensed by a dove
Perched on the hero's bronze shoulder; and suddenly
It shuddered for everyone and for itself.

6

When we are young, we're drawn to someone older.
As we grow old, we cleave to someone young.
And yet, if we would reach self-understanding,
We need to be with someone our own age.
We start as children in the shadow of
Some other person's rich experience,
And later — our experience becomes
Unwilling father to the innocence
We have elected to take under our wing.
But two innocences create experience,
Beautiful in that neither spirit lies
In the shadow of the other.

                              One morning Enrique
Was walking through the city park,
Gathering leaves, with veins, which seemed to vibrate
Alive in his hands, and suddenly he saw,
Running powerfully through the russet alleys,
Over the leaves, over thrown-away proclamations,
Through lacy shadows, over cigarette-butts,
A girl, with a serious expression,
In a clinging-wet white tee-shirt bearing
The inscription "University of Chile",
In ragged short jeans and gym-shoes.
Pushing something invisible out of her way
With her strong elbows, and hitting something
Invisible with the caps of her scratched knees,
Breathing intently, as if on sports results
Depended the whole history of the nation.

And the girl leapt in the air as she ran along
And tore off an autumn oak leaf.
She put the twig between her teeth,
Twirling it for a second like a gold propeller,
Before continuing her earnest run.
Robust, athletic, confident, she was
A little too large, but even that was good.

Enrique didn't stop to think
But turned in his tracks and ran after her,
At first seeing only her back, the notches of
Her spine rippling through the snow-white
Transparent tee-shirt. Combs and hair-clips lost,
Her hair streamed after her large powerful body
Like a Patagonian horse being chased
By its black, wiry tail. Enrique,
Through some incomprehensible superstition,
Tried to jump over her footprints
In the morning alley where the sand was patterned
By her chequered soles. Inside each print there seemed
A fragile sandy town, on no account
To be destroyed. Then he drew level with her,
With her shoulder, almost as thick as a wrestler's,
With her tense cheek to which a mole adhered
Like a coffee-grain, with her strong aquiline nose,
With her large, wind-cracked lips,
Within which each tooth sparkled
Like a freshly-washed white baby.
Enrique wanted to look her in the eyes,
But could only see her profile, her right eye
— Which was just like her mole
Except for its slightly scornful expression
Which moles fortunately don't have.
"Isn't it hard-going in a suit and shoes?"
She asked without slowing. Enrique, sweating as if
From a steam-bath, panted, "It is a bit."
"Ten miles to go," she warned him with a laugh.
"I'll make it," Enrique assured her;
"But what's at the end of the run?"
                                        "The end of the run,"
Said the girl with a grin. Enrique took off
His jacket and threw it on to the cracked wings
Of a poor marble angel, took off his shoes
And left them in the grass, having tucked his socks
Hurriedly into them, and ran on barefoot
As he had done in childhood, running through

The ebbing foam at low tide. "Won't they get stolen?"
She asked when, puffing and panting, he'd caught her up.
"I'm counting on the angels being honest.
We live in a Catholic country, don't forget."
"You believe in God?" At once both eyes,
Under their thick, imperious brows, were fixed
Mockingly on him. "In something . . ." "But what
Do you mean by something?" "I don't know exactly.
Something above us . . ." "Then, you're a mystic?"
"I'm just an artist." "What do you mean by just?"
"Just that and nothing else." "So you're one of those
Who arm themselves with a paint-brush, are you? That's
Not much of a weapon for a man."
"At least it's a clean weapon." Her elbows working
Like pistons, she asked him sharply, "Don't you think
Che Guevara's rifle was clean, then?
Which Party are you in?" "El Greco's, Bosch's . . ."
"I can't say I know it. Which Party's that?" "It's good,
But not very large. What Party are you in?"
"None at present. But I want to get things moving."
"So do I. But can't art get things moving?"
"Depends how you look at it." "And how do you?"
"I don't, very often. Haven't liked museums
Since I was a kid. Look, take your Picasso,
Who's so great, and calls himself a Communist,
But he sells his paintings to the bourgeoisie . . ."
"Picasso gives away half of his earnings
To Spanish underground fighters . . ."
"And the other half — to Chile, I suppose!
Oh, come on! His battle is just a game.
How can you expect a millionaire
To turn against other millionaires?
I prefer Gorky's storm-petrel to the dove
Of peace with absolutely everyone . . ."
"I'm also against that kind of peace. I'm sure
Picasso is too . . ." He could hardly keep pace with her,
Scorching his bare heels on the park's stone path,
And then the grit-road leading from the city.

But the girl was tireless, and brusque
Like her arm-strokes. She said, "I'm reading medicine.
Not dentistry or pediatrics: surgeons
Are what the Revolution needs . . ." "Our teeth,"
He said, "are second-class citizens,
And don't serve the revolutionary cause?
What if they become decayed and fall out
And the fighters can't chew their food?"
"Well, you don't have that problem to worry about.
You've still got your milk-teeth, *muchacho* . . ."
And she shrieked, suddenly stumbling,
And started hopping, holding on to one foot;
Then she stopped and sat down. "This is my weak spot . . ."
Her face screwed up, she nodded at her ankle.
"Good lord! I'd never have imagined you'd
Have any weak spots!" "I know what spots
You so-called men are interested in.
Just remember, as far as mine are concerned,
They're quite intact . . . Hey, get your hands off me!
I can kick just as well with a lame foot . . ."
"Calm down, I'm not going to eat your foot.
Every artist should know a little about
Anatomy, so he should be able to set bones.
Let's take a look. Gently now. Don't kick.
Your foot's not exactly Cinderella's, is it?
It wasn't intended for a crystal slipper."
"Don't think I'm made of crystal, either."
"I can see that . . . What size do you take? Elevens?"
He twisted her foot in his hands, and,
Through her tears, she said, "Are you crazy? Size six!"
He tore up his handkerchief and bound her foot
Swiftly and tightly. "This is unusual —
Bandaging a surgeon . . ." "You'd be better off
Bandaging your tongue . . ." She laced her gym-shoe
With difficulty, for her foot had swollen
A whole size, and when she tried to run again
Her foot, cruelly injuring her vanity,
Brought her up short. "Okay, we'll take a rest.

I can see you're tired, *muchacho.*" He sat down
And she fell into the grass, laughing: "*Muchacho,*
You're sitting on an ant-hill!" He jumped up,
And looked down at the cone of teeming life
He'd crushed . . . And it was someone's work, love, struggle.
But the girl went on laughing: "Now you know
What was at the end of the run — an ant-hill!"
Hiding his confusion, giving his trousers
A vigorous shake, he snapped: "We're also someone's
Ant-hill, when they squash us with their behind . . ."
"We mustn't allow it!" — She sternly raised
Her finger above her head. "We must neither be ants
Nor someone crushing ants with his behind!"
"Well, at last, that's something I agree with."
Enrique also lay down on the grass
And saw, through the grass, a brown butterfly
A couple of steps away settle on one
Of the two knolls sharply rising from her tee-shirt
Which was already slightly grass-stained.
Enrique rolled over three times
And spun head over heels, chasing away
The startled butterfly from her breast,
And drew between his lips first the tee-shirt and ants,
And then tee-shirt and skin,
Pressing fingers against fingers, ribs against ribs,
Winning her arms with his arms,
Her eyes with his eyes, her lips with his lips,
And her youth with his youth.
Tearing her arms twice out of his,
She twice pushed him away,
But the third time she couldn't tear away
And embraced him. She no longer wanted to scream.
She had liked him from the moment he threw his jacket
Over the angel's wings
Because it was stopping him from running.
At thirteen, she had turned against the church
When an old priest with a trembling, feverish hand
Had fondled her breast in the confessional.

She hated the feelings that had been aroused,
And her virginity, and all the men
Who wished to deprive her of it on the sly.
The legal sale of one's virginity
By being called wife she also found disgusting.
But her body was terribly curious,
It was aching and yearning, and reducing her
To such a state that, no matter what the shame,
Like a prostitute, she considered throwing herself
At the first man to come along,
So that she could find out what it was like —
Then she would drown herself, or join a convent.
She tried to cure herself of these desires
Of the body, which her reason judged immoral,
By studying the Revolution and by running,
But suddenly all this was overthrown.
She wanted to. Only not with just anybody
But with this funny discarder of shoes and jackets,
Who possibly had acted in that way
So that the angels could be shod and clothed.
She wanted to. Not sometime later. Now.
Through her spine the grass told her to go ahead,
There was nothing wrong in it. Was she already
In love? Perhaps. Everything in her
Suddenly became a weak spot. It flashed through her:
"If you've got to fall,
Make sure it's first from a good horse."
The sky plunged on to the grass-blades,
Without bending them at all, and the two were doubled
By nature; and from the silent ant-hill
Millions of spectators watched them.

7

Did you at nineteen love a nineteen-year-old?
Still green, their union made them ripen swiftly,
Yet this maturity was doubly youthful.
Everything in the world became multiplied
By two: eyes and arms, hair and lips,
Breathing, resentment, hope,
The wind's bite, the sea, sounds, smell, colour.
Nature flung them together in such a way
It became impossible to tell apart
The boy, the girl, and nature,
As if their crazy run without an end
Went on as it had begun. Their run
Together was a run away from something
Which bored them to death, suffocated them.
Their run together was a run over ditches,
Towards something which had never existed
But which ought to exist
Although it probably never would.
Their run together was through the age of hurry,
When everyone was running about on business,
Glancing askance at two young people running
Without an aim in view, censuring them
For their lack of purpose, as if anything in life
Is more important than becoming oneself.
It's beautiful to be running without an aim,
And for the two who were running what mattered most
Was not what they were running to — but through.
Through all the tips on how they ought to run,
Who to run after, when they ought to stop.
Through the dense crowd. Through bullets and explosives.
Through right and left wing; those who tried to trip them.
Through other people's terrors, and their own.
Through whispers that it's better to stand still.
Through all the warnings that they'd break a limb
Running at such a speed. Through the clutching
Rapacious hands on all sides, telling them:
"This way! This way!" But what is happier

Than to have nowhere to go, and everywhere?
They ran, falling together
On anything — it didn't matter what:
On the first inviting grass; iodine-scented
Seaweed; the tilted seat of a Mercedes
Abandoned in a cemetery of cars;
On the bed of a shabby hotel
In which the bedbugs, transparent from hunger,
Converged on them from the tattered wallpaper.
Enrique didn't breathe a word
To his first woman. He was too afraid.
Also he was too afraid to tell
The girl he loved about the other woman.
He now saw both of them.
He tore himself in two, rushed to and fro,
And an agonising lie was created
When he lied to one that he was busy,
And then lied to the other. He lied all the time.
It's impossible to be truthful with a woman,
But you can't deceive her in anything.
Women have an animal's scent for other women.
When women's nostrils quiver, no pumice stone
Will rub off us the alarming smell
Of another woman.
The two women, the older and the younger one,
Although they did not know about each other,
By instinct guessed the other one existed.
When she was driving by the sea one day,
Out of the car-window the older woman
Caught sight of Enrique lying beside the younger
In the sand. With a bottle of ice-cold lemonade,
Smilingly she was stroking Enrique's forehead,
Cheeks, chest and stomach. Everything dimmed
And tears welled in the eyes
Of Enrique's first woman, not the kind of tears
That freely spring, but the kind that linger,
And flow treacherously inwards.
Somehow or other she managed to drive home;

She got hold of her bottle of tranquillisers,
And wrenching off the lid, she whispered:
"You fool . . . It serves you right . . ." tossing
All the pills into her mouth.
She was saved. Enrique went to the hospital,
Stunned, shattered, broken,
Feeling like a murderer again,
And, his tears falling into her waxen hand,
Promised her something — another lie.
A lie to save oneself is a cowardly truth,
But fear of facing the cruel truth is crueller.

8

And meanwhile at the art school he attended
He was likewise split in two. His teacher there
Was an old man with a soused Bohemian charm
Who never came to work without his flask.
His strict views on the classical laws of art
Were as unchanging as the brand of cognac
Sticking out of his pocket. Never diluting
His drink with food, and unbelievably thin,
He used to joke: "When God made frames for people,
He left me in the portfolio . . ."
His coat was scorched in places, and layered with ash
Like Pompeii; and dandruff sprinkled his collar.
But in his art he was meticulous.
The least attempt to change the bounds of form
Evoked his caustic and sarcastic wit.
Art ended for him where our century
Began. He'd cry: "You want to be progressive?
Then study science or technology
Or politics, but leave art well alone.
In art, my friends, there's no such thing as progress.
But you will say — Picasso, there's progress for you.
What does that make El Greco, then — regressive?"
He worked his students till they sweated blood,
Making them draw — exact in every detail —
Now, a tomato he had brought from home,
Tobacco-flaked, bruised by his pocket-flask,
— Now, shivering yawning models, coyly asking
For a five minute break to take a pee.

Enrique loved his first teacher,
For rightly insisting on strict discipline,
But Enrique also had a secret teacher,
Old like the first, but with the difference
That he was meticulous about his clothes,
Never touched alcohol and despised all drunkards,
But in his paintings he was a subversive.
In his attic, fiery explosions warped

His canvases, and there among them mincing
— In moccasins, a dazzling white starched shirt
With the most delicately spotted tie,
A formal suit, the only one he had,
Without the slightest trace of a double crease
In trousers razor-sharp as his hair-parting —
Was the stormy old man, no taller than a doll,
The great, unrecognised demolisher
Of all established classical foundations.

He made the most incendiary speeches
So gently and velvetly, his razor-thin
Parting sparkled and blazed like a safety-fuse.
"Drawing from nature is *mierda*!" — shit:
But notice how much gentler the word sounds
In Spanish. Raising his childishly small fists,
Clenching invisible hand-grenades,
He appealed to Enrique: "You're being ineptly taught!
An artist who copies vegetables and fruit
Is committing a criminal act. They're to be eaten,
Not copied. Copying women is also stupid.
Nature's already drawn them to be slept with,
Not drawn again! . . . Under everyone's skin
In a lump we call the heart, there's a whole world.
The only one worth wasting paints on.
A photographer can't get in there.
You must imprint the invisible. An artist
Is not an observer of life — he's its creation
And creator. An artist builds by making explosions . . ."
Enrique respected both his teachers,
Listening first to the one and then the other,
But wanted a third way for himself.
He thought: "Realism is dead, it's paid the price
For immortality. And abstractionism
Has committed suicide by blowing itself up."

Enrique spent a whole year painting a canvas
Ten foot square. He called it "Water-melon".

In it, thirteen faceless pig-eyed mugs,
Armed with long predatory knives, thirsting
With all their steel for the blood of a water-melon,
Not yet a human victim, posed like mafia
Over the first gash, spilling startled seeds.
His first teacher, opening his flask,
Said: "You've betrayed all the laws of beauty.
You've begun your way in art with a betrayal.
Well, that's a dangerous start.
I know you've got another teacher,
A Lilliputian megalomaniac.
You'll have to choose between him and me . . ."

The second, velvetly raging, said to him:
"You haven't reached the heights of an explosion.
You're still a slave to verisimilitude.
Figurative . . . Figurative again . . .
I didn't suspect that you were such a coward . . .
I know you've got another teacher.
Hasn't he choked himself with brandy yet?
You'll have to choose between him and me . . ."

The world is so obsessed with suspicion,
Without betraying a soul
You can easily end up as a double Judas.

9

Enrique had two friends he'd known since boyhood.
One of them belonged to the large brood
Of a worker in a canning factory.
The other was the only son of the owner
Of a rather peculiar factory making mirrors
Which also manufactured men's braces.
The three boys had been drawn together by football.
They had chased after a battered ball,
With other children like themselves,
On a patch of waste ground, their school satchels
Democratically thrown down to make the goals.
But the satchels were of varying quality.
Some were made of imitation leather,
Which soon wore out, others were rough pigskin,
And others still were made of the softest kid;
While the satchel of a wealthy banker's son
Was even made of crocodile skin
And its lock was reputed to be real gold.
Football softens the edges of class distinction
But doesn't eradicate it, and the contempt
Of the crocodile-skin for the sensitive and proud
Imitation leather's shoddiness
Expressed itself in arrogant back-passes,
And, plagued by the contrast, the imitation
Leather didn't try to hide its grievance.
The pigskin hovered between the two.
Contemptuous of the pigskin, the kid
Was attracted to the arrogant crocodile
Yet squeaking with secret envy. But they shared
The same pitch, the same game, the same ball.
Adults can't share the same ball —
They tear it to shreds; and the pitch ceases
To be shared — everyone wants it for himself;
And they can't share the same game
Because they don't have the same rules.
When the rules differ tempers get lost,
And the players start shouting: "Ref, are you blind?"

Everyone's a foul player and the referee.
The three friends drifted apart,
But still tried to remain friends.
They went to football matches together
— Football more and more becoming
The only thing they had in common.
One of them, who had followed his father
Into the canning factory, would clearly
Go on being a tinsmith. The other friend,
Seeing no point in his father's mirrors and braces,
Was studying for the priesthood; and Enrique
Was, in his own eyes at least, a budding artist.
Sitting on a bench together, munching
Their sandwiches and uncorking a bottle of wine,
They turned from a discussion of the match
They had just watched to current politics.
Talking about football they were boys again,
Arguing about politics set that to rights . . .
The tinsmith said: "Allende's being too cautious.
You can't fight a battle slowly . . ." The priest:
"Many people would say he's going too fast . . ."
Tinsmith: "He's only giving the monopolists
A bit of a fright — which is all to the good.
I'm just afraid that's all they'll get — a fright . . ."
Priest: "And what about the frightened housewives?
They're only monopolists in their kitchens,
But they're scared to death of what tomorrow may bring.
They're buying twenty bars of soap at a time . . ."
Tinsmith: "It will take more than twenty bars
To wash off their petty-bourgeois prejudices . . ."
Priest: "All the same, people do have to wash.
When housewives feel that things are out of control,
The situation's hopeless." Tinsmith: "*Your*
Situation's hopeless. . ." Priest: "I don't understand —
What's *your*? — what's *our*? There's only the people . . ."
Tinsmith: "Don't lump me in with swinish civil servants,
Secret-police thugs, cadging, scheming priests,
Cut-throat generals, stinking thieving salesmen . . ."

Priest: "*Muchas gracias, amigo,*
For not forgetting us scheming priests . . ."
Tinsmith: "You asked for it, *amigo* . . .
The people, the people . . . A highly convenient word
For those who squat on others' necks to use:
Spouting from their pulpits how much they love us . . .
There's not a *people* anywhere in the world.
In any people there are always two peoples:
Those who squat on other people's necks
And those who hold out their necks to be sat on.
But we've got to learn not to. Marx left us
A pretty good instruction manual."
Priest: " 'Existence determines consciousness' —
How simplistic! Doesn't consciousness also
Determine our existence? Jesus Christ
Brought people together, but Marx has split the world
Into two camps." Tinsmith: "It's always been split.
But, as a matter of fact, who drove the merchants
Out of the temple? Marx? In his private life
Marx was more mild and civilized than Jesus . . ."
So they went on arguing
And banged their young fists on the peeling bench
Outside the stadium, without knowing
That very soon it would become
A prison for them both and for others,
After Allende's death.
(The young priest hid the tinsmith in his home
And was thrown into prison with him,
And then they both disappeared for good,
And their arguments vanished with them . . .)
The tinsmith had been jailed before, under Allende.
He had joined a far-left group
Assembling home-made bombs,
To give the capitalists a real fright,
Not realising that such explosions
Played into the hands of the cut-throat generals,
Giving them a pretext to suppress
Red terror with their own colour of terror, brown.

And at the time of the tinsmith's first arrest,
A vicious rumour started
That none other than the priest had turned him in,
"For friendship's sake". The terrible rumour grew.
Curling their lips in disgust, the far-left
Students from the seminary
Passed the priest by on the other side of the road.
And what provided a wry coda — his father,
The owner of the curious mirror-factory
Which also produced braces, a man
Who declared openly that in these times
You'd be well-advised to make a loop in your braces
And hang yourself in front of your mirror —
Clapped his son on the shoulder, saying:
"I hear you've shopped the tinsmith? Splendid!
I didn't think you had the guts. But I can see
You've grown up. The whole lot should be arrested,
All the Reds, with the President leading the way!"

Then the priest came to Enrique, with a hunted look.
Swaying a little, avoiding his friend's gaze,
He muttered sombrely: "Are you a friend?"
"Of course I am! You're innocent, I know."
"Then who could have spread this rumour?
Who heard us arguing after the football-match,
And made quite sure he didn't get involved?"
"I wasn't afraid to speak, if that's what you think.
It was just that sometimes he seemed right,
And sometimes you, and sometimes you both did,
And sometimes neither . . ." The young priest shook his head,
His brow pale, sweating and feverish, and moved close
To Enrique. "No, it was you who did it.
You like to think you're cleverer than us,
You want to rise in the world, and how better
Than by dragging your friend down with a lie?
You proudly stand aside from Christ and Marx.
You're the everlasting odd-man-out.
You've said to yourself: I'm a genius,

And geniuses are lifted above sin.
But these lesser mortals are capable
Of any atrocious action — like informing.
And remembering my quarrels with our friend,
You assumed I'd come to hate him,
That he was my enemy, and surely it's no great sin
To betray an enemy? . . . That's what you thought."
"I didn't, I swear . . ." "Don't add another lie.
What you did not know was that I love him
Far more than I love myself,
And it's only for that reason
That I've argued with him so much.
I've been afraid for him, as for a brother.
He wanted to change everything overnight.
He could blow up in his own hands
Like a home-made bomb, and with the splinters
Maim or kill those dearest to him, whom
He never meant to hurt — his mother, me, you . . .
Yes, I wanted to make him stop his madness,
But I'm not one of those hypocrites in a cassock
— To warn a friend by turning him in!
How does it feel — being a stool-pigeon?
You've betrayed me to the mob.
How thirsty it is for slander of this kind,
How it loves getting its fangs into
An innocent man labelled an informer!
But worse than the mob howling for your blood
Are the people who praise you for informing . . .
My own father, my braces-and-mirror-flogging dad,
Offered me his congratulations . . . That's
What you've done for me, Enrique . . ." "I swear I've not."
"Maybe you've done it and it's slipped your mind.
You're a genius. You didn't mean to do it.
Geniuses are notoriously careless.
A single word slipped out, perhaps. But now
It's branded on my forehead. And on yours!"

The door slammed painfully like a face-slap.
Enrique stood, shaking from the lie
Of his tormented friend who'd conjured it
Out of the air to drug the pain a little.
When we're insultingly accused of crimes
We haven't done, we start accusing others
And enter the vicious circle where every guiltless
Face bears the look of guilt.

Enrique jumped out of his skin — the phone rang
With an insistent, shrewish jingle.
His hand, still shaking, picked up the receiver.
"Oh, it's you, father . . ." "You remember my voice?
I thought you might have forgotten it
As you forgot that yesterday was Saturday.
I waited for you all evening. Are you ill?"
"No, but mother is . . ." "It's remarkable
How often your mother manages to fall ill
On Saturdays and Sundays, don't you think? . . ."
"She really is sick." "Couldn't you have rung me?"
"I tried to, father, but I couldn't get through.
I think your phone must have been out of order."
"There was nothing wrong with my phone. Must have been
    yours.
Caught the flu from its subscriber, I expect.
Phones can get ill too, you know, when it suits them."
Just then his mother, carrying a pipette,
Walked in in her dressing-gown. "Enrique,
Help me put in my nose-drops. I don't seem
To be able to control my hands." And instantly,
Seeing the raised receiver, she guessed right
With her female's instinct: "Oh, it's your so-called father!
Give me the phone!" She snatched it from his hand,
And in a voice booming like Ella Fitzgerald's
Said: "Would you mind not ringing when I'm ill?"
She slammed the phone down and as it quivered
She turned on Enrique: "Go on, go to him!
Leave your sick mother.

He abandoned you — do you realise that?
But you've forgiven him. Aren't you kind?
Daddy's played on your sympathy because
He's all on his own, and you've fallen for it,
Forgetting that I, your own mother,
Who didn't abandon you, am so lonely
Life isn't worth living. You don't need me anymore.
Who am I, my God? Just a useless woman,
Whom her own son doesn't want . . ." And with a tragic
Bow of her head, she stuffed the pipette
Up her nose, squeezed exactly the right amount,
And, sniffing back her sobs, went back to bed.

The phone, as if it had waited for her to leave,
Rang again. This time it breathed the well-known
Odour of his teacher's cognac and classicism:
"Here's what I've got to say to you, Enrique:
Whoever becomes friendly with a Lilliputian
Gradually becomes a dwarf himself.
You were too weak to choose between him and me,
But in art you can't be in two minds.
So I suggest that you forget me, and I
Will forgive your forgetfulness, don't worry . . ."

For a minute or two he stared at the silenced phone
In his hand, but the smell of brandy
Evaporated. Now it smelled of plastic.
That's a dead smell. Strictly, not even a smell.
He squeezed in his fist the impassive short pips,
But no sooner had he put the phone down than
The plastic means of non-communication
Shuddered again.

        With a sigh, he picked it up,
And heard: "Greetings from a terrorist! Don't worry,
I'm not in jail. They let me out today.
On bail. I've been a good boy and signed a paper
Promising not to make those dreadful bombs.

But I can still make phone-calls.
So here I am. A little whisper tells me
Our mutual friend, the fourteenth apostle,
Our friend whose motto is, Thou shalt not kill,
Squealed on me . . . Is it possible, Enrique?"
"No, it's absurd. He'd never do such a thing . . ."
"What a coincidence, I agree with you.
His conscience is too sensitive. Besides,
He's never tried to hide his opposition,
And obvious opponents don't betray.
It's those with no opinions who betray.
You see what I'm getting at?" "I'm sorry, no."
"Of course, you'd rather not see it. You recall
The day you paid a visit to my home
And saw the dynamite? Now, in your shoes,
The apostle would have raised the roof.
But you said nothing; you just took it in
With that inscrutable artistic look.
What do you do, while the fight is going on
All round you? — You continue drawing!
But perhaps you took it into your head
To put aside your oils and water-colours
For a short while, and try your hand at ink?
Such as, writing a denunciation?"
"I?" "You. Or some other artist like you
Who's listened carefully to his friends'
Political wrangles, and kept amazingly quiet?
A good listener can be a good talker too.
Forgive me, I must be honest. I'm not sure
It was you, Enrique, but I'm not sure that it wasn't . . ."
How heavy a phone is . . . Its weight could drag one
Not towards the hook nor towards the ground but into
   the ground.
Enrique put down the phone again,
But clinging with its icy black body
To his palm, the secret lines of destiny,
The lowered receiver wouldn't let go of his hands.
The young man knew it hadn't stuck for nothing.

For a time it was ingratiatingly silent,
Relaxing its invisible muscles,
Getting ready to pounce on his temples.
And then it pounced . . . In it was the same voice
Which had asked him cheerfully in the park:
"Isn't it hard-going in a suit and shoes?"
But this voice no longer belonged to her
But to the two-headed phone
In whose two heads was the same spiteful thought:
It's time to finish this off. "I'm ringing
To tell you that I've spoken to your other
Woman. What a line you've spun us both!
I'd guessed something of the sort for ages.
A heart divided like yours can't be a heart.
Don't worry, I shan't try to keep you
By taking an overdose like her. I'm strong.
I'm sorry for you, actually. You wished to run
Along two tracks at the same time. Poor boy,
You must be well and truly exhausted.
You've run yourself out. Ruined your health.
Find yourself an ant-hill to rest on,
Although one's probably not enough for you.
You'd better find two, and sit between them.
That's what you like doing, isn't it?
Now you know what's at the end of the run."
She was just slightly too large
For this world in which everything is cramped.
But how could she have shrunk
To this standard size in the hand of a clenched phone
Pounding on his temple with words?

Death has many faces . . .
                    Suicide
Cannot have only one cause.
We're not finished while there's something to cling on to,
But when there's not — we've had it! Death may wear,
At one and the same time, the face of the crowd,
The face of the age itself, of a newspaper,

Telephone, friend, the face of our father,
Our teachers' faces. Death may have the face
Of our beloved, and even our mother's face.

10

And Enrique wrote in his diary:
"I'm twenty. Life's just begun, as they say.
What's to come, though, when it's started like this?
A man is only given one soul,
But he isn't allowed to keep it for himself.
Everyone wants to slice it into shreds
As though it was meat, and each diner
Smacks his lips over his own portion
And puts his own favourite sauce on.
But while they're eating a man's soul
They're also glancing to each side jealously.
In fact, they don't just want a bigger piece,
They want the lot. And after they've eaten
They still feel hungry and bad-tempered,
And they demand another soul to carve up,
And if they can't have it they start gnawing
Their own souls, they're so hungry and spiteful.
No, I'm wrong . . . People aren't to blame.
It's the soul itself that carves itself up
And sends off the bits like magnets to draw in
Other souls, and the soul cuts these up
Into little pieces too. But why?
One soul alone can't hope to bring happiness
To all other souls at once. How good,
How easy, it must be for those without souls.
But if you have a soul, there's no way out.
I've come to understand that life is a crime.
To live is to give hurt to those you love.
On any path, we tread on ants without thinking,
And on the path of life we kill our loved ones,
Quite without meaning to, against our will,
Treading on bodies that we do not see.
Hurting people is unbearably painful.
But it's inevitable. Once you realise that,
It's logical to wish you hadn't been born.
But what do you do if you've already been born?
The most humane thing, then, is to kill yourself.

Kill yourself, to avoid killing others.
Forgive me, everyone I've killed,
Read my diary and you'll understand
That I didn't mean to, I didn't hate you,
Any of you, nor betray any of you,
That I loved you all, and love you,
And that I'm leaving you in order to express
My misunderstood love for you . . ."

Then carefully he washed his brushes,
Left his diary open on the table,
Calmly put on a clean shirt,
Stuffed his swimming-trunks sewn with a smiling penguin
Into a cellophane-bag and, going out,
Walked up to say goodbye to the water-melon
Whose bloody wound seemed still wet on the canvas
Under the predatory knives; the pig-eyes winked
At one another, and as if in a mocking gesture
Of farewell to him, the smug phone started ringing.

Enrique walked blindly through the city,
Staring down at the gleaming pavement,
Not noticing the purposeful-looking eyes
And tumours on the general's face,
Possibly General Pinochet's,
In the Ford racing along the street
And almost knocking him down.
Enrique walked to the Hotel Carrera.
The shadow of his death preceding him
Opened the doors hospitably, and in
The air-conditioned lift he pushed the button
Marked 23. Superbly situated,
The rooftop, faintly chlorine-scented, pool
Was shimmering. Strewn on air-mattresses
Were bodies in bikinis, slowly sipping
Tom Collinses. He grew less agitated,
For everybody spoke in English there.
One's native language sometimes is the last

Foothold preventing us from dying. But,
Thank heavens, it isn't possible to clutch
The straws of cocktails held in total strangers'
Falsely-occupied hands. Having got changed
In a tiny cubicle, he plunged into the pool.
He didn't swim much. He lay on his back,
His arms stretched out; but from all sides, the arms
Of other swimmers kept on striking him,
Preventing the sky from looking him in the eyes.
These strangers seemed deliberately to be trying
To jostle him to left or right, even here.
Pulling himself from the pool, with drops on his skin
Which dried immediately in the bright sun,
He paused for a moment on the very edge of the roof,
And with his tanned and tensely-arched back, heard:
"How handsome! Charming boy!" Lightly he swung
Over the rail, lightly pushed off from the edge,
Jumping as from a springboard into water.
He was a long time flying, it seemed to him.
The asphalt approached so slowly he had time
To notice, on the asphalt, a silver blaze
Of doves, and realised that he was flying
Towards them, but too late. He caught onto
Some wire, and then another, then straightway
Another, finally torturing his body
With an electric current before he died,
But those wires broke, knowing the shock was fatal.
By chance Enrique died, not on the ground
But in the air, and falling on to the road,
He who had wanted so much not to murder
When living, killed a dove with his dead body.

11

I had been to that pool many times,
Where the water was changed so regularly,
Not only, perhaps, because of germs, but so that
The water, vainly growing agitated,
Might not betray the secrets it had heard.
I read, in the Hotel Carrera,
The diary left by the self-murderer,
And his mother filled me in with other facts,
And some I worked out for myself.
Taking back the diary, his mother said:
"My son believed that by taking his own life
He would save himself from killing others.
But look what happened: with his dead body,
Senselessly, for no reason, he killed a dove.
He killed his father, who for the first time
In years I had started to feel sorry for.
He killed me. He killed the two women together.
He killed his two teachers, he killed his friends
And his talent, which was just beginning to flower.
All of us are guilty of his death,
But he, also, is guilty of killing us.
Do you have children?" I replied: "A son."
"Then it's easier for you to understand.
You, Señor, might hurt your son, without
Intending to of course, by being too busy,
Or not understanding him. You and his mother
May argue, pulling him in two directions,
Forgetting that it's tearing him apart.
And what would happen to his mother and you
If he took his revenge by taking his life?
Oh yes, we are all guilty of his death,
But heavens! how we have paid for it. Forgive me
For touching on your personal life, Señor.
There are no personal lives in the world.
Everything is linked. You are linked to me,
And linked to my dead son, although you mightn't
Have known it if I hadn't made up my mind

To come and see you. I beg you to write something
To expose the false glamour of suicide.
Art has made it glamorous. We're all so stirred
When the hero dies by his own hand, encouraging
The shameful wicked myth that it's something brave
And beautiful, and all the more appealing
Because the stage-directions make it sound
So simple: 'Stabs himself in the heart . . .'
'Shoots himself in the temple . . .' I could throttle
Those dramatists, but unfortunately most
Are beyond my reach, their throats protected by
A bronze buff collar. So write something.
If you can save a single living soul
By doing so, you will save your own . . ."
She went away; since then
She has never left my memory.

12

Snow was falling in Chile; so native to Russia,
It was alien and frightening for the Chileans.
The sentries outside La Moneda froze,
Draping their blue ears with their handkerchiefs.
Mercurio observed with satisfaction:
"This snow is a present to us from the Kremlin."
Surprised by the snow's weight, the roofs of plywood
Shanties collapsed and crashed on children's dreams.
Cars floundered through the snow to die in drifts.
The President hovered in a helicopter
Over the chaos, over the panic and cries,
The paralysed highways and the buried roads,
And landing where the snow had drifted deepest,
Allende, haggard and unshaven, seized a spade
In his awkward hands and, staggering, cleared the road
Himself, chewing the snow from his moustache
Furiously — the way he cleared the past
Like a mountain of rubble blocking the horizon;
And thus he swayed, clearing away the corruption,
Without seeing through his dirt-splattered glasses
That worms had been burrowing into the spade's tip
For so long it had crumbled, nor hearing the jibes:
"Clear it away . . . You won't clear it all away . . ."

I travelled around Chile with Pancho,
A grey-bearded drinker, an overgrown *niño*,
A one-time whaler and *mujeriego*.
Confessing his sins, he would grow softer-eyed
Than a whole drawing-room of maiden aunts.
I adored him like all the wonderful
Pure-hearted drinkers of the planet —
They are leviathans bearing on their shoulders
The earth and all its narrow-minded abstainers.
This leviathan (and ex-harpoonist) was
So powerfully gushing with stories one only needed
To attach him to a good writer. The problem was —
It turned out that he wrote on the sly himself!

His stories were now about an iceberg
On which there was a frozen grand piano,
And sometimes penguins pecking with their beaks
The slightly-stiffened keyboard extracted sounds;
Now about his first, late love — Matilda,
A prostitute with a consumptive flush
Who was his fiancée, only she died
Before the wedding; and her friends in the brothel
Collected enough money to erect
Two marble doves on her untimely grave.
In the fishing village of Punta Arenas
We spent a whole day searching for that grave,
But for some reason couldn't find it,
And went off instead to see Matilda's friends
Whom Pancho embraced and then he cried for a long time,
But no longer wanted to visit the grave.
Pancho's two basic instincts were anger and tears.
While we ate with the girls, and drank *colamono*
(Literally, "monkey's tail"), a hellish concoction
Of vodka and milk, Pancho suddenly flew
Into a towering rage against us both:
"Eujenio, while you and I sit gorging ourselves
On food and drink, our Chilean people are starving!"
And, as unexpectedly, he burst into tears,
Obliging Matilda's friends to ease his pain.
Although his gluttonous appetite was amoral
From a social point of view, and dangerous
From a medical one because of an old ulcer,
He confessed his sinfulness and ate — ate everything:
Frogs, sparrows, molluscs, but most of all
He loved *erisos* — sea-urchins fresh from the ocean;
Raw with lemon juice, salt and pepper,
They squealed in your stomach, Pancho said.
On the fishing quay at Portamona,
He bought them by the dozen, straight off a boat,
And gulped them down, with spasms of delight,
Then doubled up with pain. Resorting to
The old method of two fingers, he brought them up

And swallowed them again, exclaiming, with
Their caviare in his beard: "Eujenio,
Erisos are so wonderful! A life
Without *erisos* — can you call it life?"

When he had lain for three days
In the local hospital, having convulsions,
And, being unable to indulge in confession,
Was unexpectedly able to listen,
I took advantage of the moment
And told him the story of young Enrique
Who by committing suicide had killed
His mother and many of his dearest ones,
And the dove on the dusty road.

Seizing hold of his stomach with both hands,
As people often do when they're laughing
But now because of lacerating pain,
My friend had a fit of anger and not tears:
"What villains!" "Who?" I asked, surprised,
Straightening suffering Pancho's crumpled pillow.
"All of them are villains," he bellowed. "They all
Pushed him off the roof together . . . "
"But what about the dove?" Avoiding an answer,
The old man groaned: "I want *erisos*!"
We visited Tierra del Fuego together
When he had recovered from his *erisos*.
Swaying on mangy horses, he and I rode
Past tens of thousands or maybe millions of geese
Flying in for the winter, but Pancho muttered,
Over and over, a single word: "Dove . . . Dove . . . "
We paused by a rusty dredge, leaning over a river.
Pancho said: "You know, this river is called
Rusfin, for some strange reason. A Russian gold-
Prospector who came to Chile, God knows how,
Got drunk here, they say, and the dredge caught his sleeve
In its teeth and dragged him in. He was ground up
With the rocks. Before he died, he shrieked:

'Rus fin!' which roughly means, in broken Spanish:
The Russian's a goner . . . But perhaps it was suicide . . .
Who knows? . . . It happened so long ago . . .
Have you ever thought of suicide, *amigo*?"
"Yes, I did once . . . How about you, Pancho?"
"Ah! I love *erisos*, Eujenio.
They're a unique experience, not only
To eat, but even also to vomit them up.
I couldn't forgo them. I thought you were made
Of sterner stuff, Eujenio. I'm ashamed
To have drunk *colamono* with such a weakling.
A man should never have such thoughts. You want
To help those scum who hide their fascist leanings,
But dream of you and me together jumping
Off roofs, or putting pistols to our heads,
Hanging ourselves, or rotting our livers with drink?
You want to do their dirty work for them?
Remember, you Russian scoundrel, there's no such thing
As a hopeless situation. There's always an answer.
Nooses, bullets, jumps — they belong to a circus.
Don't you forget it. If you ever kill yourself
I'll kill you, *amigo*, I promise!"

                        His anger changed,
Without an interval, to a fit of tears:
"I'm lying to you, damn it! I too have thought
Of suicide, at times. I just didn't want
To let you think so, even for a second . . . "
Pancho and I embraced and fell silent
By the rusty dredge in whose teeth lurked
The lost secret of someone's life,
And it grew quiet all around,
As if the dead dove soared above us.

13

In my apartment that was no longer mine,
Where even the things looked at me
As if at something completely obsolete,
I once had an ultimate, dead, wistful yearning
For *erisos*, like a last wish before death.
But I remembered they weren't to be found
In Moscow's stores and restaurants.
Everything had been so shattered in my life,
I knew it could never be stuck together again.
Divorce. The loss of my son. Insults
From the mouths of former friends.
The magistrate's sympathetic, yet curious, look.
And the stream of other judges,
All of whom considered themselves "the people",
But who showed not a hint of fellow-feeling
In their quietly gleeful, accusing eyes.
Everyone there accused me of egoism,
Self-interest, moral corruption, and conceit,
Of inattention, and of not appreciating
Those whom I ought to have appreciated
Yet failed abjectly to do. No one there,
Except myself, thought of accusing me
Of murder. I was so tired of hurting people —
Relatives, women, friends. At every step
Forward or step back, to right or left,
Or even if I just stood still, it seemed
I was killing someone. And on that day
When the yearning for *erisos* overcame me,
I gritted my teeth, like a bad provincial actor
In a Chekhov tragedy, tipsily slurring:
"My friends, my dears, how can I make you happy?
How can I help you to breathe more easily?
I know I am the reason for your tears,
Although perhaps I'm not altogether at fault;
But certainly I have hurt you, and I think
It's better that I quietly withdraw . . . "

But something wouldn't let me die.
The apartment was empty. Only a dove
With almost human eyes
Was perched outside my window.
But perhaps it was the one that was killed
In Santiago under the Carrera hotel,
And dead, it had flown to my rescue,
So that I shouldn't let myself die?
There are no "foreign" disasters.
When people understand that, they will fly
Across frontiers to the rescue, like this dove,
And then there will be happiness on earth.
And then, if someone, somewhere, is unhappy —
In Santiago, Khimki-Khovrino, New York —
He still won't have the right to kill himself.
When I was young, a great poet, who amazed
Everyone by surviving into his seventies,
Said to me: "Mayakovsky and Yesenin
Criminally predicted their own deaths.
Poetry has an autosuggestive force.
My advice to you is, write whatever you like,
About whatever you like, only avoid
Predicting your own suicide."
Since then, I have placed my writing-desk
As a barricade against death. And I shall not
Be intimidated by you two
Glib salesmen — you prophet
Of pessimism, hawking despair and death;
And you merchant of lying hopes,
Pseudo-optimist. You are not really rivals,
You are in league to lure us to the edge
and crush the future with dead bodies,
Like the dove in Santiago.
Murdered Allende, I am not your judge,
I only claim to judge your murderers.

With the reprisal of immortality
Transform the extremists to self-slaughterers.
Decree with your presidential power that none
But hangmen hang themselves, and only those
Who have executed freedom on this earth
May turn their rifles on themselves, in fear.

Epilogue

It's suicide to believe that we are mortal;
Rotting under the ground's so tedious.
More shameful than lies, more ignoble than slander,
Is to make others believe that death exists.

I hate death, like Tsiolkovsky,
Who longed to reach the stars because
He wanted to populate the whole universe
With people, all equally immortal.

You will come to look upon life
As a thread which the centuries have woven.
Resurrected, as in Fedorov's vision,
Our ancestors will come to us.

They will float to us in boats and triremes.
Romulus and Remus will climb into rockets with us.
And if I die, it will only be for a short while.
I will be everywhere. Everyone. Everything.

And on the ice-crust of a distant star,
Sending signals to people in space,
I will celebrate life like the dead dove,
Soaring immortally over the earth.

1972—1978
Santiago — Moscow

Notes

p.10   **Oleg**: A prince of ancient Russia, hero of Pushkin's poem, *Song of Prophetic Oleg*. When it was prophesied that he would receive his death from his own horse, he parted with his steed. Many years later, he came to where his horse's bones were scattered. A snake crawled out of the skull and stung him to death.

p.25   **Victor Hara**: Chilean poet and singer. Imprisoned in the stadium after Allende's overthrow, he continued to play and sing. His hands were cut off, so that he could no longer play his guitar.

p.53   **La Moneda**: The presidential palace.

P.61   **Tsiolkovsky, Konstantin** (1857-1935): Russian philosopher, pioneer of international space research.

p.61   **Fedorov, Nikolai**: late 19th century idealist philosopher, who declared that mankind should unite in the struggle against disease and death. He believed that it might become possible to resurrect our ancestors.